My First Acrostic

East Midlands

Edited by Kate Gibbard

First published in Great Britain in 2009 by:

 Young**Writers**

Young Writers
Remus House
Coltsfoot Drive
Peterborough
PE2 9JX
Telephone: 01733 890066
Website: www.youngwriters.co.uk

Foreword

The 'My First Acrostic' collection was developed by Young Writers specifically for Key Stage 1 children. The poetic form is simple, fun and gives the young poet a guideline to shape their ideas, yet at the same time leaves room for their imagination and creativity to begin to blossom.

Due to the young age of the entrants we have enjoyed rewarding their effort by including as many of the poems as possible. Our hope is that seeing their work in print will encourage the children to grow and develop their writing skills to become our poets of tomorrow.

Young Writers has been publishing children's poetry for over 19 years. Our aim is to nurture creativity in our children and young adults, to give them an interest in poetry and an outlet to express themselves. This latest collection will act as a milestone for the young poets and one that will be enjoyable to revisit again and again.

Contents

The Poems

India

I n June there are monsoon floods

N ot many people survive - it's not good

D elhi is so busy

I t has so many people, it will make you dizzy

A nd it is the capital city.

Laura Mimmack & James Wilson (6)
All Saints' Primary School, Newark

India

I n June there is monsoon rain

N ot many people will survive

D elhi is busy, sweaty and hot

I n Mumbai it's a different spot

A t the centre, it's poor and rich, what a mix!

Matthew Bennett (6) & Charlotte Smith (7)
All Saints' Primary School, Newark

India

I n the morning people pray

N *amasta* the people say

D iwali is a festival, the one of light

I n the street they party day and night

A nd the fireworks, *bang* and *boom.*

William Foster (7) & Mason Buchanan (6)
All Saints' Primary School, Newark

India

I n the morning the fire flames

N ow it's time for the sun to aim

D own in the river the sun fades away

I n the night the sun has a rest in Bombay

A lso known as Mumbai.

Amelia Barlle (7) & Elizabeth Parks (6)
All Saints' Primary School, Newark

India

I n the morning it's praying time

N ow it's time for the sun to shine

D own in the town you can buy an umbrella

I t is sold by the village seller

A t night the lights are sparkling.

Dylan Cross (7) & Archie Cross (5)
All Saints' Primary School, Newark

India

I n the morning they do chalking

N ow it's lunchtime, they do talking

D eep in the night lights are shining

I n the morning the sun is blinding

A ll day parties in the street, children dancing in the heat.

Henry Hopewell & Taya Smith (6)
All Saints' Primary School, Newark

Spring

S pring makes the sunflowers grow tall

P eople start to wear sunglasses

R ain in the spring

I n the spring the flowers come up tall

N ests are made in the trees

G rass grows.

Sophie Homer (6)
Dovedale Primary School, Nottingham

Spring

S pring makes the flowers grow tall

P eople start to wear sunglasses

R ain glows in the sun

I t is hotter in the day

N ow it is sunny

G ames are fun to play.

Edward Allen (5)
Dovedale Primary School, Nottingham

8

Spring

S pring is really hot

P addling pools come out

R ain waters the flowers too

I n spring bees come out of their beehives to make honey

N ests come out of garden trees

G et *buzzing.*

Finlay Brown (6)
Dovedale Primary School, Nottingham

Spring

S pring is hot and people wear sunglasses

P addling pools come out

R ain lets the flowers grow

I n spring bees come out

N ests come in trees

G et *buzzing.*

George Farmer (6)
Dovedale Primary School, Nottingham

Spring

S pring is hot and the bees come

P eople can wear short-sleeved T-shirts

R abbits can come out of their cages

I n spring flowers grow

N ight in spring is a bit lighter

G row seeds and flowers.

Jack Rogers (6)
Dovedale Primary School, Nottingham

Spring

Spring is hot, so you don't have to wear long sleeves

People start to wear sunglasses

Rabbits come out to play and hop around

In spring bees come out

Nests come in trees

Get *buzzing.*

Abigail Webster (5)
Dovedale Primary School, Nottingham

Spring

S pring is when you can put a barbecue on

P eople start to wear sunglasses

R ain in spring

I n the spring flowers grow

N oises are made by things

G rass grows.

Aliyah Francis (6)
Dovedale Primary School, Nottingham

Spring

S pring is hot and you can wear sleeveless tops

P eople sunbathe

R ain waters the flowers

I n spring you can go to the beach

N oises go away

G oats come out to play.

Tyler Barrell (5)
Dovedale Primary School, Nottingham

Spring

S pring - bees start to come out

P eople start to wear sunglasses

R ain - wet

I n spring you play outside

N ests in the trees

G o out - you can have fun!

Cerys Orme (5)
Dovedale Primary School, Nottingham

Spring

S pring makes the flowers grow tall

P eople start to wear sunglasses

R ain in the spring

I n the spring the flowers come out

N ow in the spring the birds make their nests

G rass grows more.

Ellie Marshall (5)
Dovedale Primary School, Nottingham

Spring

S pring makes the flowers grow tall

P eople get out their sunglasses

R abbits come out to play and to peep around

I n spring bees come out

N ests come in trees

G et *buzzing*.

Jaimie MacLeod (5)
Dovedale Primary School, Nottingham

Spring

S pring can make flowers

P eople come outside

R abbits come out

I don't want to get stung by bees

N ests in gardens

G et some trees.

Jessica Douglas (6)
Dovedale Primary School, Nottingham

Spring

S pring makes the birds come out

P eople wear T-shirts

R abbits come out to jump

I n spring the children come out to play

N oises come out

G oats come out.

Alex Varney (6)
Dovedale Primary School, Nottingham

Spring

Ⓢ pring makes people go swimming

Ⓟ eople go sunbathing

Ⓡ abbits come out

Ⓘ like the flowers that grow

Ⓝ ests appear in trees

Ⓖ ets fresher.

Nadia Aicha (5)
Dovedale Primary School, Nottingham

Fire

F ire can kill you

I t is dangerous

R unning fire

E ating fire.

Harry Stevenson (7)
Firfield Primary School, Derby

Earth

E arth can wobble very strongly

A nd Earth can hurt us

R attling Earth

T he Earth shakes

H eavy shaking.

Ben Gotts (6)
Firfield Primary School, Derby

Fire

F ire is as hot as lava

I t can kill you

R eally, really hot

E ven hotter than an oven.

Megan Colley (7)
Firfield Primary School, Derby

Earth

E arth can shake

A nd rocks are heavy

R ocks roll very fast

T housands of people live on Earth

H umans live on the Earth.

Otto van Huizen (6)
Firfield Primary School, Derby

Earth

E arth can wobble and shake

A nd Earth can be destroyed

R ocks can hurt us

T iny people can die by earthquakes

H aving lots of things can kill us.

Eben Clara Goode (7)
Firfield Primary School, Derby

Water

 ater is wavy

A nd cold and wet

T ouches your face

E veryone gets soaking wet

R ainforest.

Avani Johal (6)
Firfield Primary School, Derby

Air

A ir is as cold as ice

I always need a snug coat

R eally, really freezing ice.

Eliza Charnock (6)
Firfield Primary School, Derby

Fire

F ighting fire

I 'm afraid

R ed hot

E arth burns.

Benjamin Franklin (7)
Firfield Primary School, Derby

Earth

E arthquakes are made by plates moving

A scary sight

R un away! Flaming hot, it's a fire!

T here's an earthquake

H *ah!* Tricked you!

David Smedley (6)
Firfield Primary School, Derby

Fire

F ireworks are as fast as lightning

I ce can melt when fire's near it

R apid fire as hot as lava

E arth can burn.

Benjamin Bywater (7)
Firfield Primary School, Derby

Water

W ater races as fast as lightning

A walrus is an animal

T hat lives in the sea - it looks like a huge seal

E ating an ice cream on the beach

R acing across the sand.

Ambrin Lea Chapman (7)
Firfield Primary School, Derby

Fire

 ire is hot

I t's dangerous

R acing fires

E verywhere around you.

Manuv Holloway (7)
Firfield Primary School, Derby

Earth

E arth has rainforests in it

A frica is a continent in this world

R are animals all around

T iny animals can die in earthquakes

H ow we live we need Earth.

Luke Morris (7)
Firfield Primary School, Derby

Earth

E arth makes rainforests

A nts live on Earth

R oaring tornado

T housands of people live on Earth

H umans are on Earth.

James Tew (7)
Firfield Primary School, Derby

Air

A ir is so brilliant like ice

I would look silly if I were air

R ocket air is so cool.

Jacob Hackett (6)
Firfield Primary School, Derby

Air

A ir is like a helicopter

I t blows you away

R aging through me.

Hayden Rhodes (7)
Firfield Primary School, Derby

Air

A ir is strong

I t can blow you away

R aging a fury.

Aidan Poole (6)
Firfield Primary School, Derby

Water

W ater is good for everything

A ll the time it is flowing

T ime is nothing to it

E normous waves

R ushing as fast as the wind.

Amy Huntley (7)
Firfield Primary School, Derby

Water

W ater is wet

A nd it is blue

T urn the cold tap on

E very time it pours

R ushing to you.

Adam Melvin & Jack Cook (7)
Firfield Primary School, Derby

Water

W obbly waves bubbling up and down

A lways swishing like washing

T ingling and as blue as paint

E xciting, clear, wobbly water

R aging, rushing through a waterfall.

David Hedley (7)
Firfield Primary School, Derby

Fire

F lames as hot as can be

I ndestructible fire as red as can be

R ed hot fire rolling down

E nergetic fire as red as can be.

Sophie Peel (7)
Firfield Primary School, Derby

Fire

F ire is red as jelly

I nvidual flames dancing like a human

R ed fire is red as a flame

E nergetic fire flames.

James McKeown (7)
Firfield Primary School, Derby

Water

W avy water flows around

A frog jumps in and splashes

T adpoles wriggle around

E verywhere there are lily pads

R ushing water flows around.

Kathryn Inskip (7)
Firfield Primary School, Derby

Water

W ater is cold as an ice cube

A lways going like a cheetah

T urning around the corner

E normous high water

R ushing like a tiger.

Jack Fantom (6)
Firfield Primary School, Derby

Fire

F ire is red flames

I have never gone near fire

R ed hot flames are very hot

E asy to make fire.

Arianna King (7)
Firfield Primary School, Derby

Earth

E arth is strong like iron

A n earthquake makes huge craters

R olling down everything in its path

T ragic death to people

H uge boulders.

Jack Shaw (7)
Firfield Primary School, Derby

Fire

F lames go flaming around in this fireplace

I t is red as a ruby

R ed as a red swing

E normous elephant with big red ears.

Ria Khosse (6)
Firfield Primary School, Derby

Earth

E arthquakes happen on Earth

A s big as the sun

R ound as a tennis ball

T ime is on Earth

H armful gases on Earth.

Oliver Dodic (7)
Firfield Primary School, Derby

Trees

T rees grow

R oots grow

E verything grows

E verywhere

S eeds.

Matthew Cooper (4)
Horsley CE Primary School, Horsley

Leaf

L eaves on stalks

E verywhere

A nd on

F lowers.

Abbe Brown (4)
Horsley CE Primary School, Horsley

Petal

P etals on flowers

E very flower

T hey are special

A nd pretty

L ovely.

Tallulah Colclough (4)
Horsley CE Primary School, Horsley

Sun

S un shines

U mbrellas up

N ight-time.

Abby Bondon (4)
Horsley CE Primary School, Horsley

Roots

R oots

O utside

O ver there

T rees

S uck the water.

Charlie Dave (4)
Horsley CE Primary School, Horsley

Mud

M ud is dark
U nder the ground
D irty mud.

Jack Smith (5)
Horsley CE Primary School, Horsley

Seed

S eeds, seeds, I love you

E veryone loves you

E veryone loves you

D o you grow?

Callum Allton (5)
Horsley CE Primary School, Horsley

Sun

S un
U p high
N ear the sky.

Ayesha Wilkinson (6)
Horsley CE Primary School, Horsley

Stem

S tems give drinks
T o the flowers
E veryone
M agic.

Daniel Woodings (5)
Horsley CE Primary School, Horsley

Sun

S un, sun, I love you

U p in the sky

N ever go away.

Grace Pollard (5)
Horsley CE Primary School, Horsley

Flowers

F lowers good, flowers bad, brill flowers

L ove you, I care for you

O live seeds I plant

W et soil on the grass

E very day you grow for me

R ight in my garden

S oil, your dream.

Evie Marriott (6)
Horsley CE Primary School, Horsley

Sunlight

S un makes the food

U nder the sun it grows

N ight needs the moon

L eaves drink the water

I f I give a plant some water it will grow

G row, grow, grow

H igh, high, high

T o the sky.

Jack Harper (5)
Horsley CE Primary School, Horsley

Leaf

L eaves are green
E verywhere
A nd red
F lowers grow.

Nathan Hill (6)
Horsley CE Primary School, Horsley

Seeds

S eeds, seeds, we need you

E very time

E very night

D o you like plants?

S eeds, I love you.

Millie Pollard (5)
Horsley CE Primary School, Horsley

All About Me

J umping all over the place

O pen his boxes all the time

S wimming in the water meadows on Sundays

E ating a hot dog every Friday

P ractising karate

H ot in summer.

Joseph Samuels (6)
Lake View Primary School, Mansfield

All About Me

O range is my favourite colour

L ake View is my school

I like Demi and Libby

V ery much

I like Mrs Rangcroft being

A teacher.

Olivia Smith-Duffin (7)
Lake View Primary School, Mansfield

All About Me

L ikes to write books
I like to feed my dog
B all bouncing
B rownies
Y ellow yo-yos.

Libby Taylor (6)
Lake View Primary School, Mansfield

George

G oes shopping all the time

E yes are blue

O range is the colour of my hair

R otten sometimes

G ood at numeracy

E ggs are my favourite food.

George Clarke (7)
Lake View Primary School, Mansfield

Joseph

J oyful and happy

O utside and inside

S unny day, go and play

E njoy the rain

P lay in the park

H elp my horse.

Joseph Bagshaw (7)
Lake View Primary School, Mansfield

Michael

M agic

I like ice cream

C ool

H appy, I like

A pples

E at meat

L ike my mum.

Michael Moss (7)
Lake View Primary School, Mansfield

Jasmine

J am tarts

A good girl

S un hurts my eyes

M orning

I have a super mum

N ice time for horses

E ggs are good to eat!

Jasmine Strouther (6)
Lake View Primary School, Mansfield

Megan

M y best friend is Olivia

E yes are blue-green

G reen is my favourite colour

A girl I am

N ever naughty.

Megan O'Hare (7)
Lake View Primary School, Mansfield

Kayleigh

K ind

A t the park

Y ellow bag

L ollipops

E yes are blue

I n a dance

G o to school

H ome is good.

Kayleigh Ward (6)
Lake View Primary School, Mansfield

Ryan

Red is my favourite colour

Young and handsome

And hair is blond

Nice and kind.

Ryan Noble (6)
Lake View Primary School, Mansfield

Tyler

T alks

Y o!

L ikes to read

E yes are brown

R eally good at maths.

Tyler Woollands (6)
Lake View Primary School, Mansfield

Demi

 ancing, I like

E lephants, the

M oon,

I gloos.

Demi Chuter (7)
Lake View Primary School, Mansfield

Lee

L ate for school sometimes

E xcellent intelligence

E yes are a greenish-blue

C hucks everything in his room

H ates girly programmes

U nhappy on rainy days

T oo happy on sunny days

E xcellent at maths

R aces around outside.

Lee Chuter (7)
Lake View Primary School, Mansfield

Cain

C razy Cain

A ccurate at football

I ncredible Cain

N uts at tidying my room!

Cain Stendall (7)
Lake View Primary School, Mansfield

Joshua

J umping gymnast

O lder than my brother

S illy

H airy

U seful

A ctive!

Joshua Williams (6)
Lake View Primary School, Mansfield

Dylan

D oesn't like writing

Y ou are cool

L ikes catching

A m a boy

N o, I am a ball!

Dylan Mitchell (7)
Lake View Primary School, Mansfield

Libby

L oves stinky cheese

I n Class 2

B rilliant at maths

B rilliant at numeracy

Y oung and seven years old.

Libby Bartlett (7)
Lake View Primary School, Mansfield

Daniella

D istracting

A lways asleep

N anny is the best

I n Class 2

E normous heart

L oves lollies

L ate for school sometimes

A m bad and good.

Daniella Knight (6)
Lake View Primary School, Mansfield

Daniel

D umb at catching

A t Rainworth for 5 years

N uts at catching balls

I mpressed with his work

E yes are blue

L ikes football and basketball.

Daniel Colledge (7)
Lake View Primary School, Mansfield

Arron

A t home

R un outside

R ides a bike

O n my Xbox

N ever eats bananas.

Arron Hill (6)
Lake View Primary School, Mansfield

Ethan

E yes are blue

T oo good to be true

H ow cool

A nnoying Ethan sometimes

N ever funny enough!

Ethan Fisher (6)
Lake View Primary School, Mansfield

Jack

J ack eats junk

A m I cuckoo?

C uckoo Jack

K ing Kong, I am.

Jack Halstead (6)
Lake View Primary School, Mansfield

Doggies

D ifferent colours

O n my bed

G ood friends

G reat paws

I n my bedroom

E very one soft

S mooth, cuddly.

Abbie Wilkinson (5)
Leen Mills Primary School, Nottingham

Lego

L ego, all colours

E very brick different

G ood fun

O n the floor.

Spencer Kent (6)
Leen Mills Primary School, Nottingham

Teddy

T eddies, all brown

E ars floppy

D oes lots of talking

D reams on my bed

Y ou and me.

Jordan Bradshaw (5)
Leen Mills Primary School, Nottingham

Lego Car

L ego is my favourite toy

E very vehicle I like

G oes together

O ne of them looks cool

C rashes into bits

A re your cars like mine?

R ace around.

Joseph Gillan (7)
Leen Mills Primary School, Nottingham

Bratz Doll

B ratz dolls make me happy

R ocking clothes make them hot

A mber is what I call my doll

T he sad one is Chloe

Z any boots

D o you have a Bratz doll?

O n my shelf

L ooking good

L ots of friends.

Amber Richardson (7)
Leen Mills Primary School, Nottingham

Aeroplane

A eroplanes fly

E ven mine

R oar goes the engine

O range wings

P anels of blue

L ong journey

A eroplanes have wheels

N ight-time flights

E arly wake up.

Daniel Hary (6)
Leen Mills Primary School, Nottingham

Doll's House

D olls are made out of plastic

O pen windows

L oads of dolls live in a doll's house

L ots of doors

S ee through window

H ow do you dolls speak?

O pen doors

U p and down the stairs

S hare with your friends

E veryone inside.

Ku Hany Ahmad-Daud (6)
Leen Mills Primary School, Nottingham

Soldiers

S oldiers are very brave

O bey the sergeant

L ots of them

D ressed in green

I n my box

E veryone different

R eady for a fight

S leepy soldiers.

Daniel Radford (7)
Leen Mills Primary School, Nottingham

Lego Boat

L ego is rough and bumpy

E very bit is different

G reen bits

O range sails

B est present

O cean waves

A lways break

T ake time to build.

Joshua Vere (6)
Leen Mills Primary School, Nottingham

Pram

P ram full of dolls

R ound wheels

A round the garden

M iles of fun.

Tayla Stonley (6)
Leen Mills Primary School, Nottingham

Hot Wheels

H ot wheels are hard

O pen roads

T he wheels are round

W hizz about

H ave big tyres

E very one is different

E ach one has colour

L oads of fun

S peeding on the track.

Taylor Radford (5)
Leen Mills Primary School, Nottingham

Lego Castle

L ego castle is hard to make

E very bit different

G o up in my room

O nly me

C annonballs firing

A rmour metal plated

S couting enemies

T elling plans

L ots of men

E verything great fun.

Luke Pykett (7)
Leen Mills Primary School, Nottingham

Dinosaur

D o you have a dinosaur?

I n my bedroom

N ibble your fingers

O n the shelf

S pecial to me

A dinosaur spiky tail

U p in the sky

R oars and roars.

Toby Symms (7)
Leen Mills Primary School, Nottingham

Rocket

R ocket ships fly to the moon

O n zero they blast off

C an you see him in space?

K eep the ship away from the sun

E verybody likes my toy rocket

T he rocket is my favourite toy.

Charlotte Sladden (6)
Leen Mills Primary School, Nottingham

Train Set

T rain sets are pushed by children

R aky is my favourite metal train

A train is black or red

I t is good because it has oval, wide wheels

N ow he races round the track

S ome train sets are really good

E ngines and carriages make a train

T rains are really fun to play with.

Ellie Christian (6)
Leen Mills Primary School, Nottingham

T-Rex

T -rex is a fierce dinosaur

R ex has sharp teeth

E veryone is terrified of him

X has scary eyes.

Connaugh Maclachlan (6)
Leen Mills Primary School, Nottingham

Planets

P lanets are in space

L ive Pluto

A planet good

N ow Jupiter is careful

E arth is for people

T ime is running out

S pace is where people explore.

Urate Ramadani (6)
Roe Farm Primary School, Chaddesden

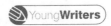

Planets

P lanets move around the sun

L oads of planets move around the Earth

A ll of the planets spin around

N eptune is blue and it is big

E arth is blue and green

T he planets move around

S un is big and it is bright.

Holly Williamson (6)
Roe Farm Primary School, Chaddesden

Myself

M ost of the time I play with my friends

Y esterday I hurt myself

S ometimes we go on school trips

E very day I go to the park

L ove my baby sister

F riends are fantastic.

Sorcha Bunting (6)
Roe Farm Primary School, Chaddesden

Planets

P luto is a very little planet

L argest planet is colourful Jupiter

A stronauts have visited the moon

N obody has been to the hot sun

E arth is green, blue, white and yellow

T here are nine large planets.

Lorik Ramadani (7)
Roe Farm Primary School, Chaddesden

Space

S aturn has a glass water ring

P luto is the smallest planet

A steroids float around

C omets look like shooting stars

E arth, white, blue and brown.

Macauley Burley (7)
Roe Farm Primary School, Chaddesden

My School

M ake me a beautiful picture please

Y esterday I had fun

S ometimes I work hard

C an I help you?

H ope you have fun at school today

O utside is very sunny

O nly 12pm

L ast week we had the school play.

Tamara Black (7)
Roe Farm Primary School, Chaddesden

Planets

P lanets and spacemen

L oads of people live on Earth

A round the Earth is the moon

N eptune is pretty

E arth is not flat

T oo many people

S ome planets may have life.

Callum Hickton (6)
Roe Farm Primary School, Chaddesden

Planets

P lanets are out in space

L ots of planets go around the sun

A sun is hot

N ow the planets are big

E arth is where everyone lives

T he sun is big

S un is very, very strong.

Zhiting Zeng (6)
Roe Farm Primary School, Chaddesden

Planets

P lanets go around

L ots of planets like Earth

A liens

N eptune

E arth is better than Pluto

T idy Earth

S pace machines in space.

Louipiero Stasiak (6)
Roe Farm Primary School, Chaddesden

Planets

P lanets rotate around the sun

L ots of different planets rotate around the sun

A ll different colours on the planets

N eptune is very blue in space

E arth is for people

T ime is running out

S pace has lots of planets.

Connor Greatorex (6)
Roe Farm Primary School, Chaddesden

Planets

P lanets go around the sun

L ots of planets in space

A way in space

N eptune is a blue planet

E arth is blue and green

T wo aliens were on the moon

S pace is full of planets.

Isabelle Pearce (6)
Roe Farm Primary School, Chaddesden

Planets

P luto is a small planet

L ots of planets

A ll planets are near the sun

N eptune is blue

E arth is a medium planet

T he planets go around the sun

S aturn has got lots of colours.

Charlie Gregory (5)
Roe Farm Primary School, Chaddesden

Planets

P lanets are dark

L iving creatures live on Earth

A liens roam

N eptune

E arth is the best planet

T he Earth

S pace machine is in space.

Harry Doman (6)
Roe Farm Primary School, Chaddesden

Mercury

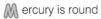ercury is round

E mpty holes

R ed planet

C olour is red

U p in space

R eally red

Y es, I like Mercury.

Abigail Burridge (7)
Roe Farm Primary School, Chaddesden

The Sun

S un is not a planet

U p in the sky

N o, it does not move.

Imarni Whitby (7)
Roe Farm Primary School, Chaddesden

The Moon

M oon is in space

O n the moon

O r going to the moon

N ight-time.

Christieleigh Riddings (6)
Roe Farm Primary School, Chaddesden

Planets

P lanets are round and some have rings around

L ook at the planets and look at the colours

A star is shining

N o planets are black

E arth has more water than other planets

T he planets are different colours

S ome people live on Earth.

Leah Tatam (6)
Roe Farm Primary School, Chaddesden

Mercury

M oon comes out at night

E veryone looks at moonlight

R ed planets

C raters

U p in the sky

R ockets fly up in space

Y ay, Mercury.

Jamie-Lee Kelly (6)
Roe Farm Primary School, Chaddesden

Little Red

L is for little, she is extremely tiny

I is for intelligent, she is clever

T is for tidy, she likes things clean

T is for ticklish, she's so ticklish

L is for lovely, she is so nice

E is for excited, she is excited about everything

R is for reliable, you can make her do anything

E is for eager, she wants to do everything

D is for delightful, people love her.

Reece Witts (6)
Stenson Fields Primary School, Derby

Little Red

L is for lovely

I is for incredible

T is for TV

T is for trees

L is for lazy

E is for excited

R is for rainbow

E is for everybody

D is for different.

Teagan Spray (6)
Stenson Fields Primary School, Derby

Little Red

L is for lovely

I is for incredible

T is for tea

T is for trees

L is for likeable

E is for everybody

R is for ready

E is for excited

D is for different.

Keaya Inneh
Stenson Fields Primary School, Derby

Little Red

L is for lovely, she is pretty

I is for intelligent, she is clever

T is for tidy, she is tidy

T is for ticklish, she is it

L is for little, she is small

E is for everyone, she likes everyone

R is for rosy, she has got red cheeks

E is for excited, she is happy

D is for delightful, she is very nice.

Kane Tisdall (6)
Stenson Fields Primary School, Derby

Little Red

L is for little, she is very small

I is for incredible, she's so incredible

T is for tidy, she loves to tidy

T is for trust, everybody can trust her

L is for lovely, she is so kind

E is for excited, she is so excited

R is for the red, her favourite colour is red

E is for excellent, she knows a lot of everything

D is for delightful, she is very nice.

Simran Ark (6)
Stenson Fields Primary School, Derby

Little Red

L is for lazy
I is for incredible
T is for truthful
T is for tidy
L is for lucky
E is for eager

R is for red
E is for excited
D is for delightful.

Alfie Clarke
Stenson Fields Primary School, Derby

Little Red

L is for loveable
I is for incredible
T is for tidy
T is for ticklish
L is for lazy
E is for everybody

R is for rosy
E is for excited
D is for delightful.

Jake Hawkins (6)
Stenson Fields Primary School, Derby

Little Red

L is for loveable

I is for intelligent

T is for ticklish

T is for tremendous

L is for lazy

E is for eager

R is for red

E is for excited

D is for different.

George Bailey-Wainwright (6)
Stenson Fields Primary School, Derby

Little Red

L is for little, she is very small

I is for intelligent, she is smart

T is for tea, she likes a cup of tea

T is for tidy, her clothes are neat

L is for lazy, she likes it in bed all day

E is for excited to go to Grandma's

R is for red, it is her best colour

E is for eager, she can't wait

D is for Daddy, she loves him very much.

Blake Bowman (7)
Stenson Fields Primary School, Derby

127

Little Red

L is for lovely, she is so beautiful

I is for incredible, she is so fantastic

T is for typical, she always gets things her way

T is for tiny, she is tiny

L is for line, she is so straight

E is for knowing everything, she is so clever

R is for rugby, it is her favourite sport

E is for excellent, she is good at everything

D is for delightful, she never lies.

Dilan Takhar (6)
Stenson Fields Primary School, Derby

Little Red

L is for little, she is extremely small

I is for incredible, she is fantastic at everything

T is for ticklish, she loves being tickled

T is for tidy she likes everything nice and clean

L is for likeable, she likes everybody in the world

E is for eager, she is eager for everything

R is for red, she wears everything that's red

E is for excited, she is excited about everything

D is for delightful, she is delighted to relax.

Naiya Kellesa Hutchinson (7)
Stenson Fields Primary School, Derby

Little Red

L is for lovely

I is for intelligent

T is for TV

T is for tidy

L is for likeable

E is for excited

R is for running

E is for energy

D is for delightful.

Oliver Wisdom (6)
Stenson Fields Primary School, Derby

Little Red

L is for little, she is small

I is for intelligent

T is for tiny, a tiny girl

T is for tea, she likes to drink tea

L is for lovely, a lovely little girl

E is for easy

R is for run

E is for every little girl

D is for dainty, a dainty little girl.

Simran Sandhu
Stenson Fields Primary School, Derby

Little Red

L is for lovely
I is for incredible
T is for ticklish
T is for tidy
L is for likeable
E is for excited

R is for red
E is for excellent
D is for delightful.

Ben Beresford (7)
Stenson Fields Primary School, Derby

Little Red

L is for lovely, she's always kind

I is for incredible, she is very smart

T is for tired, she always runs

T is for tidy, she's always neat

L is for little, she is very small

E is for excellent, she loves visiting people

R is for red, it's her favourite colour

E is for exciting, always dances

D is for delightful, she is happy wherever.

Aaron Dhillen (7)
Stenson Fields Primary School, Derby

Little Red

L ovely

I ncredible

T icklish

T idy

L ikeable

E xcited

R osy

E ager

D elightful.

Ethan Cox (6)
Stenson Fields Primary School, Derby

Little Red

L is for lovely Little Red

I is for intelligent Red

T is for ticklish Little Red

T is for tiny Little Red

L is for likeable, she loves everybody

E is for excited, she bounces about

R is for red, she loves red

E is for excellent, she does excellent SATs

D is for delightful, she is very kind.

Amar Singh Sandhar (6)
Stenson Fields Primary School, Derby

Little Red

L ovely, she is a nice girl

I ntelligent, she is a smart girl

T asty, she ate all the cakes

T icklish, because she was born like that

L ively, she ran all the way

E ager, she loves to please people

R ed, it's her favourite colour

E xcited, she loves going to Granny's

D elightful, she makes everyone smile a lot.

Alexander Collyer (7)
Stenson Fields Primary School, Derby

Little Red

L is for late, she is not very fast

I is for intelligent, she is very smart

T is for tired, she can't stay awake

T is for ticklish, she can't resist a tickle

L is for little, she's not very tall

E is for excited, she loves going to people's houses

R is for riddle, she plays lots of jokes

E is for eager, she can't wait for some things

D is for delightful, she is a nice little girl.

Bryan Thompson (6)
Stenson Fields Primary School, Derby

137

Little Red

L is for little, she is quite small

I is for intelligent, she is very clever

T is for ticklish, she giggles a lot

T is for tiny, she is quite small

L is for lovely, she is very kind

E is for eager, she loves to please people

R is for red, she always wears it

E is for excited, she loves meeting people

D is for delightful, she loves to delight people.

Amrit Ark (6)
Stenson Fields Primary School, Derby

Little Red

L is for lovely because she is small

I is for intelligent because she is smart

T is for ticklish because she is giggly

T is for tasty because she is hungry

L is for likeable because we all adore her

E is for eager because she always pleases everyone

R is for red because it is her favourite colour

E is for excited because she likes visiting people

D is for delightful because she makes everyone happy.

Charlie Trail (7)
Stenson Fields Primary School, Derby

Little Red

L is for lovely, she is so cute
I is for incredible
T is for tidy, she is very neat
T is for ticklish, she giggles a lot
L is for likeable, we all adore her
E is for excited, she makes everybody happy

R is for red, it is her favourite colour
E is for eager, she likes to please people
D is for delightful, she makes everyone pleased.

Lauren Greenway (6)
Stenson Fields Primary School, Derby

Little Red

L is for luxurious
I is for intelligent
T is for ticklish
T is for tragic
L is for little
E is for extraordinary

R is for rosy
E is for excited
D is for delightful.

Lauren Barnett (7)
Stenson Fields Primary School, Derby

Little Red

L ovely, she's always nice

I ncredible, she helps people

T idy, she is neat

T ired, she is lazy

L oving, she's always sweet

E xcited, she always jumps around

R ed it is her best colour

E xcellent, she is clever

D elightful, she is nice.

Caleb Dhamrait (7)
Stenson Fields Primary School, Derby

Little Red

L ovely, she is nice

I ncredible, she is fast

T icklish, she laughs

T ired, she is sleepy

L oveable, she likes everyone

E xcited, she is excited

R ed

E xtremely good

D elightful.

Eli Anne Orchard
Stenson Fields Primary School, Derby

Little Red

L is for nice little girl

I is for incredible

T is for tired, she is always sleepy

T is for ticklish

L is for lovely, she is always nice

E is for excited, she always loves visiting

R is for red, it is her favourite colour

E is for excellent, she is always giving

D is for delightful.

Libby Hirst (5)
Stenson Fields Primary School, Derby

Little Red

L is for lovely, Little Red is lovely

I is for intelligent, she is very smart

T is for toffee, she smells like toffee

T is for talented, she is very good at it

L is for likeable, we all adore her

E is for eager, she likes to please people

R is for red, it's her favourite colour

E is for excited, she loves visiting people

D is for delightful, she smiles a lot.

Rosemary Nwauzu (6)
Stenson Fields Primary School, Derby

Little Red

L is for little, she is very cute

I is for impressive, she is very flexible

T is for ticklish, if you tickle her she will laugh a lot

T is for tickle monster, she is very good at tickling

L is for lovely, we all love her

E is for excited, she gets very excited

R is for red, she always wears red

E is for excellent, she always tries to help

D is for delightful, she always tries her best.

Daniel Wells (7)
Stenson Fields Primary School, Derby

Little Red

L is for lovely, she makes people giggle

I is for incredible, she helps people

T is for tidy, she has straight hair

T is for ticklish, laughs all the time

L is for likeable, always takes things to poorly people

E is for excited, she is always ready for fun

R is for rosy, she is always red

E is for eager, she talks when she isn't allowed

D is for delightful, she always makes people laugh.

Jack Gratton (6)
Stenson Fields Primary School, Derby

Little Red

L is for little girl

I is for intelligent, she is very good

T is for tasty, she is greedy

T is for ticklish, she giggles every day

L is for lovely, she is beautiful

E is for extraordinary, she is busy

R is for red, it is her favourite colour

E is for eager, she helps people and makes them happy

D is for delightful, she is helpful.

Paige Robinson (7)
Stenson Fields Primary School, Derby

Great Fire Of London

G unpowder blowing up all the houses

R ed sky like the pencil crayon

E verywhere is red

A lways blowing away

T aller every minute

F ire burning wood on the houses

I n the city of London

R acing in the air

E verywhere there is ash

O ven, that was burning, blew down the baker's shop

F lames all around

L ots of people escaped

O n the way only nine people died

N ow everybody knows

D emolished every home

O n foot, carriage and boat

N aughty flames died down.

Nathan Clarke (7)
William Levick Primary School, Dronfield

Great Fire Of London

G igantic flames spreading around

R eeling up into the air

E ating their way through

A lcohol exploding

T aller and taller every second

F lashing up and down

I n the bakery it started

R ed flames dancing around

E verywhere is in flames

O nly nine people died

F lying fire everywhere

L ondon was dying

O n 1666 it started

N o one liked it

D iary of Samuel Pepys was buried

O h how the fire raced

N ot a lot of people died.

Lily Collinson (7)
William Levick Primary School, Dronfield

Great Fire Of London

G iant flames

R acing through the air

E verywhere was covered with flames

A ll over the streets

T aller by every minute

F lashing in the air

I n that big city

R acing from the bakery

E very house was destroyed

O nly nine people died

F lames dancing in the sky

L ots of people escaped from the fire

O n carriage, by foot and boat

N one of the people wanted their house to be destroyed

D isaster could have been so much worse

O nly real danger was fire

N early four hundred years ago.

Alyssa Widdowson (7)
William Levick Primary School, Dronfield

Great Fire Of London

G igantic flames dancing in the air

R ed water

E veryone running for safety

A sh raining everywhere

T aller by the hour

F lames blazing everywhere

I n the city of London

R eally happened back in 1666

E veryone survived except nine

O ver everything raged naughty flames burning houses down

F ire hot, no one dared to put it out

L ots of people escaped

O n went the fire

N o one dared to put the fire out still

D emolished homes every minute

O n the streets of London

N ever to be forgotten.

Lydia Denton (6)
William Levick Primary School, Dronfield

Great Fire Of London

G igantic flames

R ising in the air

E verybody screaming madly

A sh falling from the sky

T o the ground

F ire

I gnoring Samuel Pepys

R eally happened in 1666

E verybody was panicking

O nly started with a little mistake

F lames all around

L ots of people escaped

O nly nine people died

N ever been seen again

D emolished all the houses

O n went the fire

N ever will be forgotten.

Ben Kingham (7)
William Levick Primary School, Dronfield

Great Fire Of London

G unpowder blowing up houses in a blaze of glory

R acing through the night sky

E ating dynamite every hour

A sh falling from the air

T ouching the fiery sky

F lickering in the morning air

I gnoring Samuel Pepys' advice

R acing in the wooden house streets

E verybody trying to help

O xygen was needed in the great fire

F lames all around

L ots of people escaped

O nly an oven set London ablaze

N ever been a bigger fire

D emolished every home

O n foot, carriage and boat they escaped

N aughty flames died down and it finished.

Ewan Spencer (7)
William Levick Primary School, Dronfield

Great Fire Of London

G unpowder blowing houses up

R ising flames into the air

E very time exploding

A sh

T owers of fire

F lames all around

I gnoring Samuel Pepys

R acing through the air

E very minute it was getting bigger

O ver eight people died

F lames were catching the wood

L ondon was burning

O range and red flames

N o one escaped

D emolished all the houses

O vens were burning

N o one looked back.

George Washbourne (7)
William Levick Primary School, Dronfield

Great Fire Of London

G igantic flames in the air

R emember King Charles I

E verywhere was ash falling from the sky

A ll the air was red

T he water was red too

F lashing in the air

I n the city of London

R ed water was passed down in buckets

E veryone except nine lived

O n Pudding Lane a baker started it

F lames got bigger

L ots of people escaped by foot

O r carriage and boats

N o one looked back and was brave enough

D emolished the houses

O nly it could have been worse

N early thousands of people stayed alive.

Chloe Morrell (7)
William Levick Primary School, Dronfield

Great Fire Of London

G igantic

R ising up

E xtremely

A ll were rushing everywhere

T all in the sky

F lames in the sky

I nside a bakery

R ushing everywhere

E verybody running

O n September 1666 began the fire

F lames dancing in the sky

L ots of gas

O ver London

N ever seen again

D ashing through the sky

O n went the fire

N ever killed anyone except . . .

Katherine Ducker (7)
William Levick Primary School, Dronfield

Great Fire Of London

G igantic flames flying fast

R aising in the air

E veryone got out

A sh on the floor

T he fire was everywhere

F lashing in the air

I ncredible flames in the sky

R eally killed nine people

E veryone got away by foot, carriage or boat

O n Pudding Lane

F rom a bakery

L ondon was demolished

O n September 1666

N early every house was knocked down

D ashing ash everywhere

O n the sky was ash

N o one could stop the fire.

Dougie McElhattan (7)
William Levick Primary School, Dronfield

158

Great Fire Of London

G igantic flames whooshing through the air

R ushing through the streets

E ating the homes up

A ttacking everything

T all flames

F ire

I nside the bakery

R ed water

E verywhere

O n the London Bridge

F lames dancing in the sky

L ondon was burning down

O h no

N early burning all the houses up

D own London streets

O n went the fire

N o people died, except nine.

Victoria Knowles (7)
William Levick Primary School, Dronfield

Great Fire Of London

G unpowder blowing up

R aining ash

E ating the houses

A lways getting bigger

T here were houses demolished

F lames getting bigger every minute

I n the city of London

R aced down the streets

E verywhere was aflame

O ver 400 years ago

F ire still blazing fiercely

L ondon lighter than ever

O nly nine people died

N othing stopped it

D emolishing houses

O ven in the bakery burning

N othing could be seen except for flames.

William Earl (7)
William Levick Primary School, Dronfield

Great Fire Of London

G igantic flames

R acing around the air

E verywhere was red

A shes everywhere

T aller than ever

F lashing all day

I n the city of London

R ushing everywhere

E verywhere there was ash

O ven that was burning London down

F lying with the ash

L ots of people escaped

O n and on the fire went

N othing could stop it

D ied?

O nly nine people

N early 400 years ago.

Ben Vandrill (7)
William Levick Primary School, Dronfield

Great Fire Of London

G igantic flames

R ed water

E ating their way through the town

A sh was everywhere

T he fire was spreading quickly

F lames everywhere

I nside the bakery shop

R ed sky

E verywhere

O n every street there was fire

F ire was everywhere

L ondon houses got demolished

O nly nine people died

N o one could stop the fire

D ancing in the sky

O n Pudding Lane it started

N early everybody escaped.

Alexander Swift (6)
William Levick Primary School, Dronfield

Great Fire

G igantic flames spreading in the air

R acing through the air

E ating through the houses

A sh everywhere on Pudding Lane

T he fire was spreading

F lames destroyed houses

I nside was alcohol

R eal flames

E verywhere.

Ben Cornwell (6)
William Levick Primary School, Dronfield

Great Fire Of London

G igantic flames

R ed and orange

E verywhere

A s big as could be

T he fire was spreading

F ire went up in the sky

I n Pudding Lane

R ed sky

E verywhere houses got knocked down

O n every street there were houses on fire

F lames destroying the streets

L ondon houses got demolished

O n went the fire

N obody could stop the fire

D ashing through the sky

O h, nine people died

N ow the fire is dying.

Ella Danson (6)
William Levick Primary School, Dronfield

Great Fire Of London

G reat fire of London

R acing flames

E ven Samuel Pepys knew it was bad

A ngry flames

T errible flames

F lames

I n the sky

R aging

E verywhere

O ver the streets

F ire escapes

L ike red flags in the sky

O ver the houses

N ever go to London

D on't go there

O r you will get hurt

N ow it is safe.

Heathcliff Vaughan (6)
William Levick Primary School, Dronfield

Great Fire Of London

G igantic flames

R emember 1666

E verywhere

A sh was everywhere

T he houses got demolished

F lames everywhere

I nside the bakery

R ed sky

E verywhere covered in ash

O ver the town was ash

F rom house to house it went

L ots of people escaped

O n carriage or by foot and boat

N early every house

D estroyed

O n Pudding Lane, help, help

N ot many people died.

Jonathan Blake (7)
William Levick Primary School, Dronfield

Great Fire Of London

G reat fire

R acing through the streets

E veryone was scared

A sh everywhere

T ake the water to the flames

F lames flying

I n the sky

R acing for the street

E veryone thought they would die

O ver the sky

F lames everywhere

L ight the sky

O ver the houses

N obody was safe

D on't go there

O r you will die

N ot a very nice place.

Christian Wooller (7)
William Levick Primary School, Dronfield

Great Fire Of London

G igantic flames in the air

R acing through the sky

E verywhere to be seen

A lways getting bigger

T ouching the sky

F lying in the sky

I t started in a bakery

R ed in the sky

E ndless buildings destroyed

O nly started by a little oven

F lames ignited in a bakery

L ots of people escaped

O n foot, by boat

N ine people

D estruction could have been so much worse

O h dear it was

N ot good to be there.

Jonathan Redfern (6)
William Levick Primary School, Dronfield

Great Fire

G igantic flames

R aging through the streets

E ating the houses

A ll on Pudding Lane

Travelling through Pudding Lane, it happened in a bakery

F amous fire people remember

I nside the bakery

R emember Samuel Pepys' diary

E very day.

Josh Tranter (7)
William Levick Primary School, Dronfield

Tooth Fairy

T ooth

O range dress

O ver the clouds

T winkle

H elpful

F abulous

A t night

I n bed

R ainbow

Y ou are beautiful.

Ellie Rawson (5)
William Levick Primary School, Dronfield

Tooth Fairy

T eeth
O ver the clouds
O nly at night
T akes them to the castle
H elps them find the tooth

F airy
A ride on the doves
I n the window
R ich
Y ellow wand.

Abby Shipley (5)
William Levick Primary School, Dronfield

Tooth Fairy

T eeth

O ver clouds

O nly at night

T he tooth fairy collects treasure

H er hair is golden

F luttering

A lways magical

I nvisible

R ides on a rainbow boat

Y ellow dress.

Thomas Mirfin (5)
William Levick Primary School, Dronfield

Tooth Fairy

T eeth

O ver clouds

O range wings

T winkling

H appy

F abulous

A t night

I nvisible

R ainbow

Y ellow wand.

Jacob Smith (5)
William Levick Primary School, Dronfield

Tooth Fairy

T eeth
O ver the clouds
O nly at night
T iny
H ouse

F ly
A lone
I n the night
R ainbow sail
Y ellowy golden hair.

Matthew Mallett (6)
William Levick Primary School, Dronfield

Tooth Fairy

T eeth
O ver the clouds
O nly at night
T reasure and gold
H appy and helpful

F airy and fast
A mazing and exciting
I n the window
R ich
Y ellow wand and yellow wings.

Grace Shaw (6)
William Levick Primary School, Dronfield

Tooth Fairy

T eeth, she likes teeth

O h, she likes to fly

O ver the clouds

T winkling tooth fairy

H elpful, oh helpful

F riendly as can be

A mazing, she is amazing

I ncredible tooth fairy

R eally, really kind

Y ellow wand and wings.

Jessica Ward (6)
William Levick Primary School, Dronfield

Tooth Fairy

T eeth

O nly at night

O ver the beautiful clouds

T winkling stars on her dress

H onest all the time

F aint as can be

A nxious not to wake people up

I nvisible to see

R ainbow coloured wings

Y ellow coloured wand.

Joel Gregory (6)
William Levick Primary School, Dronfield

Tooth Fairy

T eeth

O range

O ver the clouds

T aking

H elpful

F airies

A tooth fairy collects teeth

I n your bed

R ainbow sails

Y ellow wings.

James Crossley (6)
William Levick Primary School, Dronfield

Tooth Fairy

T ooth

O ver the clouds

O nly

T iny

H ouse

F ly

A lone

I n the window

R ainbow

Y ellow hair.

Ava Templeman (5)
William Levick Primary School, Dronfield

179

Tooth Fairy

T eeth
O h she likes teeth
O ver the clouds
T winkling like a star
H onest all the time

F aint as can be
A s faint as can be
I ncredible tooth fairy
R ainbow sails
Y ellow wand.

Oscar Bayliss (6)
William Levick Primary School, Dronfield

Tooth Fairy

T ooth

O ver the wall

O range dress

T ooth fairy

H elpful

F ly freely

A t night

I s incredible

R eally famous

Y es, she has sparkly wings.

Daniel Brown (5)
William Levick Primary School, Dronfield

Tooth Fairy

T ooth
O ver the clouds
O nly at night
T iny
H elpful

F riendly
A lone
I nvisible
R are
Y ellow wand.

Tomas Bairstow (5)
William Levick Primary School, Dronfield

Tooth Fairy

T eeth

O range dress

O nly at night

T ooth fairy

H elpful

F lies

A t night

I n bed

R ainbow sail

Y ellow wand.

George Jones (5)
William Levick Primary School, Dronfield

Young Writers Information

We hope you have enjoyed reading this book - and that you will continue to enjoy it in the coming years.

If you like reading and writing poetry drop us a line, or give us a call, and we'll send you a free information pack.

Alternatively if you would like to order further copies of this book or any of our other titles, then please give us a call or log onto our website at www.youngwriters.co.uk.

Young Writers Information
Remus House
Coltsfoot Drive
Peterborough
PE2 9JX
(01733) 890066